THE FUNNY THING ABOUT FOOTBALL

A COLLECTION OF GAME DAY CARTOONS AS FEATURED IN THE ARKANSAS DEMOCRAT-GAZETTE

Published by

Arkansas Democrat 🛡 Gazette

Arkansas' Largest Newspaper

Published by

Arkansas Democrat ✠ Gazette

Copyright © 2012, *Arkansas Democrat-Gazette*, Inc.

Printed in the United States of America

Compiled by Dusty Higgins

Illustrations by Matt Haney, Vic Harville and Dusty Higgins

Special contributions by Wally Hall

Designed by Norma Edwards

Coordinated by Tabitha Cunningham

Edited by Rhonda Owen and Randal Hunhoff

WEHCO Publishing
121 E. Capitol Ave.
Little Rock, AR 72201

FORWARD

The first time I saw a sports cartoon was in my journalism class at Bryant Sr. High School back in the '90s when Vic Harville was drawing them. At the time I was focused on drawing editorial cartoons and comic strips for the school newspaper, *The Prospective,* under the magnificent direction of adviser and teacher Margaret Sorrows. The thought of drawing a cartoon for a football game had never occurred to me. The idea of two mascots dueling and exchanging witty banter was weird, bizarre, completely fascinating. I was hooked.

Reading Harville's cartoons during those formative years helped develop my attachment to the Razorbacks and the University of Arkansas, where I would later attend college.

During my first visit to the campus and the journalism department, I met journalism adviser Dr. Patsy Watkins who, after looking at my portfolio of cartoons, explained to me that the college newspaper, *The Arkansas Traveler,* would actually pay me to draw cartoons. It was a new concept for me. I certainly wasn't paid for drawing cartoons in high school and, honestly, I probably would have done it for free in college. (Note to my current bosses: I've got a wife, kid and mortgage now. That deal is no longer on the table.)

While I attended college, Vic Harville left the *Arkansas Democrat-Gazette* for Donrey Media Group (later Stephens Media Group), where he continued drawing Razorback cartoons up until 2010. Matt Haney began his stint as sports cartoonist for the *Arkansas Democrat-Gazette* in 2000. As a student, I remember picking up the paper every game day and not only reading the cartoons, but studying them. What makes this cartoon work? How does it relate to the events surrounding the game? How do you draw legs on an anthropomorphic Razorback? Fingers or hooves? Weird stuff like that.

College gave me the opportunity to experiment in the way I approached sports cartoons. My most memorable experiment was based on a design in which each cartoon that season connected end to end to create an entire football field, complete with a stadium full of cheering Razorbacks. It was a bit ambitious and didn't work as well as I meticulously planned. For one thing, midway through the season the paper couldn't afford color for the sports section, so that cartoon ran in black and white. In 2005, Matt Haney would leave the *Arkansas Democrat-Gazette* and a space opened in the graphics department. I jumped at the chance. A couple of months later I found myself drawing the sports cartoons I used to read and working with a fantastic team of veteran sports editors and writers, including Wally Hall, Jeff Krupsaw, Mike Smith, Bob Holt and Tom Murphy.

I was an ambitious kid. Still am. But if you had asked that 16-year-old kid sitting at the drafting table in the Bryant High School journalism classroom if he thought he would be drawing cartoons for the *Arkansas Democrat-Gazette* in just a few years, I think he would have said no. "They've already got plenty of talent," he would have said. "They don't need me when they've got talent like Harville."

Throughout its storied history, the *Arkansas Democrat-Gazette*, and the two papers that preceded it, have had some fantastic cartoonists on its staff draw the Razorbacks: Jon Kennedy, George Fisher, John Deering, Vic Harville and Matt Haney. Unfortunately, because of the way things were archived we have very few printable cartoons available dating before 2000. This book collects cartoons from the most recent sports cartoonists — Harville, Haney and myself.

It's truly humbling to have my cartoons placed next to those brilliant cartoonists who inspired me to follow in their footsteps. I've had the pleasure of both reading these cartoons and creating them. I hope you enjoy them as much as I have.

Woo Pigs!

Dusty Higgins

DUSTY HIGGINS

Dusty Higgins is an Arkansas native and University of Arkansas graduate living in Bryant, Ark., with his wife, Kristin, and their daughter Kahlan. His cartoons and illustrations have appeared in several Arkansas newspapers including the *Arkansas Democrat-Gazette*, the *Northwest Arkansas Times*, the *Benton County Daily Record* and the *Arkansas Times*. Higgins has illustrated several graphic novels and books, including the Pinocchio Vampire Slayer series, *Knights of the Living Dead*, and *The Way of Oz: A Guide to Wisdom, Heart, and Courage*.

MATT HANEY

Born in Oklahoma City, Okla., in 1975, raised in Omaha, Neb., Matt Haney attended the University of Nebraska-Lincoln and graduated with a bachelor's degree in fine arts with an emphasis in painting and graphic design. Haney left the *Arkansas Democrat-Gazette* in 2005 to work as a newspaper graphic artist and illustrator, comic artist, painter and cartoonist at his hometown newspaper, the *Omaha World Herald*. Haney is heavily influenced by pop culture, particularly comic books, animation, science fiction and horror films from the 1920s-60s, as well as Japanese monster movies and superhero television shows of the 1950s-70s.

VIC HARVILLE

Vic Harville graduated from Texarkana High School in Arkansas and attended the University of Arkansas on a track scholarship. Harville joined Stephens Media Group in June 2000 after 12 years with the *Arkansas Democrat-Gazette*. His cartoons have won several awards and honors. His work has been reprinted in *Newsweek*, the *Washington Post*, and *USA Today*. It has also been featured on NBC's *Prime Time Live* and ABC's *Dateline* and *Good Morning America-Sunday*. Three books of his cartoons have been published: *That's The Way To Run A War*, *We Knew Bill Clinton* and *Rounding up the Usual Suspsects*. Harville retired from Stephens Media Group in 2011.

CONTENTS

THE BOWL CLUB

The Arkansas Razorbacks have a long and storied history in postseason bowl games having played 39 times in postseason, including in eight states ranging from California to Florida. A bowl game gives our artists plenty of opportunity for creativity, which you will see in great abundance in this chapter. Get ready to smile at the memories.

—Wally Hall, Assistant Managing Editor/Sports for the Arkansas Democrat-Gazette

ARKANSAS 31, MICHIGAN 45

LAS VEGAS BOWL - JANUARY 1, 1999 *by Vic Harville*

After a 9-2 season that had boosted Arkansas' stagnant football program, the No. 11-ranked team had an opportunity to boost themselves even higher with a bowl win over No. 15 (and defending national champion) Michigan.

ARKANSAS 20, EAST CAROLINA 17 (OT)

LIBERTY BOWL - JANUARY 2, 2010 *by Dusty Higgins*

Arkansas played East Carolina for the first time in the Liberty Bowl. In the previous year's Liberty Bowl, East Carolina lost to Kentucky.

ARKANSAS 42, MISSISSIPPI STATE 21

NOVEMBER 21, 2009 *by Dusty Higgins*

Arkansas (6-4) faced off against a 4-6 Mississippi State team that was desperate for a win in its bid to qualify for bowl status. After losing to Mississippi State in 2008 for the first time in a decade, and with a three-game winning streak under Coach Bobby Petrino, Arkansas wasn't planning on making it easy on the Bulldogs.

3

ARKANSAS 14, WISCONSIN 17

CAPITAL ONE BOWL - JANUARY 1, 2007 *by Dusty Higgins*

Arkansas was ranked as high as No. 5 during the season and had a 10-game winning streak before losing its last two games to LSU and Florida in the SEC Championship game.

ARKANSAS 43, AUBURN 65

OCTOBER 16, 2010 *by Dusty Higgins*

No. 7 Auburn was among 13 unbeaten teams going into the game against No. 12 Arkansas. Both teams were among four SEC West members (including LSU and Alabama) in the top dozen in The Associated Press poll.

5

ARKANSAS 26, OHIO STATE 31

SUGAR BOWL - JANUARY 4, 2011 *by Dusty Higgins*

This game marked the first Bowl Championship Series appearance for the No. 8 Razorbacks as they faced No. 6 Ohio State, who had up to that point a 0-9 record against SEC teams in bowl games. Off the field, Ohio State had been dealing with NCAA investigations concerning players selling memorabilia that led to an announcement that five players would be suspended the first five games the following season. They were still, however, eligible to play in the Sugar Bowl.

ARKANSAS 7, MISSOURI 38

COTTON BOWL - JANUARY 1, 2008 *by Dusty Higgins*

Head coach Houston Nutt had already packed his bags and moved off to Ole Miss by the time the Razorbacks had rolled into Cotton Bowl Stadium to play No. 6 Missouri for their bowl game. The game was also marked with athletic director Frank Broyles' retirement after 50 years at Arkansas and the almost-certain exit of two-time Heisman Trophy winner Darren McFadden.

ARKANSAS 35, OLE MISS 3

NOVEMBER 13, 2004 *by Matt Haney*

With both Arkansas and Ole Miss sporting 3-5 records, only the winner of the game would be able to continue advancing toward the goal of playing in a bowl game.

ARKANSAS 21, SOUTH CAROLINA 34

NOVEMBER 8, 2008 *by Dusty Higgins*

The Razorbacks, in their first year with Bobby Petrino, were determined to reach a bowl game. Although both teams featured top passing offenses, each led by redshirt sophomores, the Gamecocks were missing three key starters due to injuries.

9

ARKANSAS 29, KANSAS STATE 16

JANUARY 6, 2012 *by Dusty Higgins*

While Big 12 fans lamented not getting a chance to face an SEC team in the BCS title game (which ended up being a rematch between No. 1 LSU and No. 2 Alabama) the Cotton Bowl did give them a chance to see how Big 12's No. 8 Kansas State fared against SEC's No. 6 Arkansas.

ARKANSAS 28, FLORIDA 38

December 2, 2006 *by Dusty Higgins*

Arkansas' third trip to the SEC title game gave the Hogs their first realistic chance to win it. In the two earlier attempts, Arkansas lost 34-3 to Florida in 1995 and 30-3 to Georgia in 2002.

BEST OF THE SEC WEST

The SEC West has developed into the best division in the best conference in all of college football — that was not missed in this chapter. An all-time favorite is here and features a powerful rival, the Crimson Tide of Alabama. SEC division foes always pluck deep at the heartstrings of Razorbacks fans and that brings out the very best in our artists.

—*Wally Hall, Assistant Managing Editor/Sports for the* Arkansas Democrat-Gazette

ARKANSAS 38, MISSISSIPPI STATE 31 (2 OT)

NOVEMBER 20, 2010 *by Dusty Higgins*

The Razorbacks were 3-1 in SEC road games as they headed to Starkville to take on the Mississippi State Bulldogs. The Bulldogs had just lost their previous game 30-10 to Alabama. Meanwhile, a Mississippi State booster had told the NCAA he had received a message from Auburn quarterback Cam Newton's father that outlined a payment plan to bring the quarterback to Mississippi State, which was part of an ongoing controversy at Auburn.

OCTOBER 13, 2007 *by Dusty Higgins*

Both teams carried two conference losses and were looking to secure a win for SEC title contention but Auburn had a slightly better record. Arkansas sought to change its status with a big win.

ARKANSAS 24, MISSISSIPPI STATE 21

NOVEMBER 20, 2004 *by Matt Haney*

The 1:30 p.m. afternoon kickoff for the Mississippi State (3-6) game was the seventh different kickoff time for the Razorbacks (4-5) in 10 games. Starts ranged from 11 a.m. to 8 p.m. throughout the season.

ARKANSAS 38, AUBURN 14

OCTOBER 8, 2011 *by Dusty Higgins*

Both No. 10 Arkansas and No. 15 Auburn, the defending BCS national champion, were looking for
an SEC West victory to keep them at the top of the SEC West standings with LSU and Alabama.

NOVEMBER 7, 1998 *by Vic Harville*

At 7-0, the Razorbacks were having a winning season and confidence was high as they headed into the game against 6-2 Ole Miss.

ARKANSAS 44, OLE MISS 8

OCTOBER 20, 2007 *by Dusty Higgins*

Halfway through the season, Arkansas and Ole Miss were both winless in SEC games.

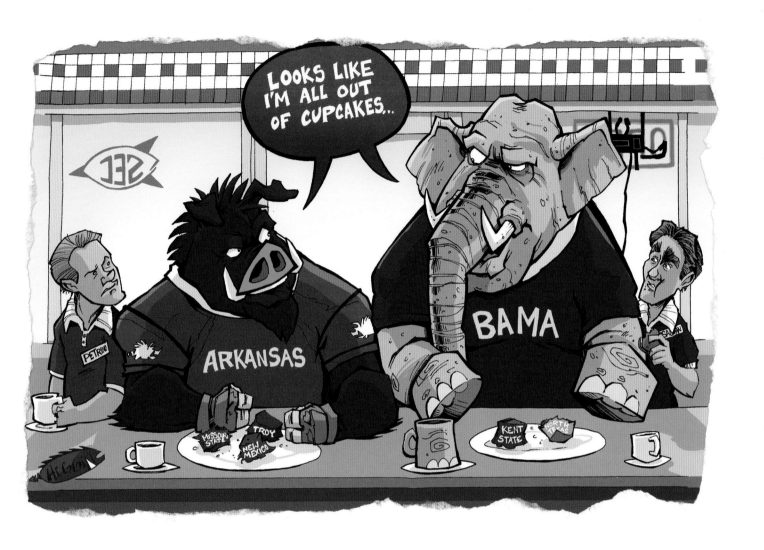

ARKANSAS 14, ALABAMA 38

SEPTEMBER 24, 2011 *by Dusty Higgins*

SEC heavyweight No. 3 Alabama faced off against No. 14 Arkansas at Bryant-Denny
Stadium after each going 3-0 in their first games against nonconference foes.

ARKANSAS 19, AUBURN 21

OCTOBER 28, 2000 *by Matt Haney*

The 4-2 Razorbacks had lost seven consecutive road games going into the game against 6-2 Auburn at Jordan Hare Stadium.

ARKANSAS 28, MISSISSIPPI STATE 14

NOVEMBER 18, 2006 *by Dusty Higgins*

Arkansas had to win against Mississippi State to clinch the SEC West title, but after coming off an open date and an unexpected win against Alabama two weeks earlier, MSU was setting itself up to be a trap game.

ARKANSAS 44, MISSISSIPPI STATE 17

NOVEMBER 19, 2011 *by Dusty Higgins*

The game against Mississippi State gave No. 6 Arkansas the chance to complete its first unbeaten home season since 1999. Arkansas was 8-0-1 all-time against the Bulldogs in Arkansas.

ARKANSAS 42, ALABAMA 6

SEPTEMBER 26, 1998 *by Vic Harville*

Arkansas had a running game ranked first in the SEC to pit against an Alabama defense ranked second nationally.

ARKANSAS 21, MISSISSIPPI STATE 22

NOVEMBER 21, 1998 *by Vic Harville*

After outplaying, then losing in the last three minutes of their previous game against Tennessee, an 8-1 Arkansas hoped to make up for it with a win against 6-5 Mississippi State, which would also guarantee Arkansas the SEC West title.

ARKANSAS 25, AUBURN 22

OCTOBER 11, 2008 *by Dusty Higgins*

Both Arkansas and Auburn were in a rut going into this game, Arkansas having lost its previous three games by a combined 108 points while Auburn was struggling to kick-start its offense.

ARKANSAS 20, AUBURN 38

OCTOBER 16, 2004 *by Matt Haney*

After losing two of their top offensive players, junior right tackle Zak Tubbs and running back Peyton Hillis, to injuries, the Razorbacks faced a tough 6-0 Auburn team.

ARKANSAS 27, ALABAMA 10

SEPTEMBER 25, 2004 *by Matt Haney*

The game against Alabama marked the start of eight consecutive SEC games for the Razorbacks. It was the first time Arkansas had played eight consecutive SEC games since joining the conference for the 1992 season.

ARKANSAS 7, ALABAMA 35

SEPTEMBER 26, 2009 *by Dusty Higgins*

Arkansas (1–1) headed to Bryant-Denny Stadium to tackle a No. 3 Alabama team (3–0) that also happened to be a 17 1/2-point favorite.

COMING SOON

TO AN ALABAMA STADIUM NEAR YOU

Arkansas VS the

CRIMSON TIDE

REAARH

THE BEASTS IN THE SEC EAST

With regional cuisine that includes boiled peanuts and mustard-based barbecue sauce, traveling through the SEC Eastern Division has always been interesting. Not playing those schools on a regular basis could have created extra drama, but what you get in this chapter is insight with good taste and a strong sense of humor.

—*Wally Hall, Assistant Managing Editor/Sports for the* Arkansas Democrat-Gazette

ARKANSAS 31, VANDERBILT 28

OCTOBER 29, 2011 *by Dusty Higgins*

Having been outscored in the first halves against Texas A&M and Ole Miss before rallying for victories, Arkansas was desperate to upgrade its offensive performance against a Vanderbilt team that was no pushover, having intercepted 15 passes in seven games.

ARKANSAS 27, KENTUCKY 20

OCTOBER 3, 1998 *by Vic Harville*

Arkansas and Kentucky, sporting new coaches Houston Nutt and Hal Mumme respectively,
were off to their best starts in the past decade. Arkansas had just beaten Alabama 42-6.

ARKANSAS 41, GEORGIA 52

SEPTEMBER 19, 2009 *by Dusty Higgins*

After winning their first game and an open week, the Razorbacks were amped and ready for their SEC opener at home against a Georgia team that was 24-4 in SEC road games under coach Mark Richt.

ARKANSAS 30, FLORIDA 45

OCTOBER 2, 2004 *by Matt Haney*

Arkansas traveled to "The Swamp" to play No. 16 Florida in what is considered one of the toughest and loudest stadiums to play in the SEC.

ARKANSAS 24, TENNESSEE 28

NOVEMBER 14, 1998 *by Vic Harville*

Both No. 10 Arkansas and No. 1 Tennessee were
8-0 going into the game at Neyland Stadium, in
what many believed would be a preview of the
SEC Championship game.

36

SEPTEMBER 16, 2006 *by Dusty Higgins*

Arkansas' defense appeared pretty solid after their first two games, but had yet to force a single turnover going into the game against Vanderbilt.

ARKANSAS 7, FLORIDA 38

OCTOBER 4, 2008 *by Dusty Higgins*

As of this game, Florida was the only SEC team that Arkansas hadn't beaten since joining the SEC in 1992. After suffering sizable losses to Alabama and Texas in previous games, the chances of Arkansas beating No. 12 Florida didn't look too promising.

ARKANSAS 14, GEORGIA 20

OCTOBER 23, 2004 *by Matt Haney*

Arkansas was 0-2 in October, and things weren't looking promising as they headed into the match against No. 10 Georgia.

ARKANSAS 31, GEORGIA 24

SEPTEMBER 18, 2010 *by Dusty Higgins*

Georgia had lost its previous week's game against South Carolina, but was still considered a 2 1/2-point favorite as No. 12 Arkansas rolled into Athens for its first SEC game of the season.

ARKANSAS 49, VANDERBILT 14

OCTOBER 30, 2010 *by Dusty Higgins*

Despite being much tamer than Arkansas offensively, averaging 9.5 points in SEC games and ranking 105th in the country in passing, scoring and total offense, Vanderbilt had beaten Ole Miss 28-14 — the same margin of victory that Arkansas beat Ole Miss by the week before.

ARKANSAS 49, TENNESSEE 7

NOVEMBER 12, 2011 *by Dusty Higgins*

The fortunes for the No. 8 Razorbacks and the unranked Volunteers had changed drastically since their last meeting in 2007. At the time, Tennessee was in the midst of qualifying for its fifth SEC Championship game, while the Houston Nutt regime was teetering at Arkansas. As the 2011 game began, Tennessee was 0-5 in SEC games, while Arkansas was 4-1.

NON-CONFERENCE GAMES

Call them cupcakes or Sisters of the Poor but the Razorback Nation gets up for nonconference games. The Razorbacks are usually highly favored but that just gave our artists a challenge. Some of the illustrations were prophetic, as you will see.

—Wally Hall, Assistant Managing Editor/Sports for the Arkansas Democrat-Gazette

ARKANSAS 26, SMU 0

SEPTEMBER 4, 1999 *by Vic Harville*

The 18th-ranked Razorbacks were picked to win the SEC West in the preseason poll. Their first game of the season marked the final scheduled game with Arkansas' former SWC opponent, SMU.

ARKANSAS 44, TENNESSEE TECH 3

SEPTEMBER 4, 2010 *by Dusty Higgins*

The Razorbacks were the overwhelming favorite to beat Tennessee Tech in the first game of the 2010 season.

ARKANSAS 38, LOUISIANA–LAFAYETTE 17

SEPTEMBER 5, 1998 *by Vic Harville*

The Razorbacks started their 105th season against Southwestern Louisiana,
which had finished the previous season with a 1-10 record.

ARKANSAS 63, EASTERN MICHIGAN 27

OCTOBER 31, 2009 *by Dusty Higgins*

It seemed appropriate that the scariest thing to impersonate trick-or-treating in Arkansas might be as Marc Curles' officiating crew, now infamous for their controversial calls that favored No. 1 Florida in a close game earlier in the season.

ARKANSAS 31, LOUISIANA-MONROE 7

SEPTEMBER 11, 2010 *by Dusty Higgins*

Having just destroyed nonconference opponent Tennessee Tech in the previous game, the Razorbacks were eager to keep the momentum going against Louisiana-Monroe before heading into the next week's game against SEC opponent Georgia.

ARKANSAS 58, FLORIDA INTERNATIONAL 10

OCTOBER 27, 2007 *by Dusty Higgins*

Against a Florida International team on a 19-game losing streak and after choppy performances against both conference and nonconference opponents earlier in the season, the concern in Arkansas wasn't winning so much as making sure the team looked good while doing it.

ARKANSAS 20, TEXAS 22

SEPTEMBER 11, 2004 *by Matt Haney*

After beating Texas the previous season, Arkansas was looking at the Texas game with hopes that a win would mark the start of a winning season.

ARKANSAS 49, LOUISIANA-MONROE 20

SEPTEMBER 18, 2004 *by Matt Haney*

Although the game would be played at War Memorial Stadium in Little Rock, Arkansas would be considered the "away" team in a deal with Louisiana-Monroe that would help it maintain its NCAA Division I program status.

ARKANSAS 48, NEW MEXICO STATE 20

NOVEMBER 15, 2003 *by Matt Haney*

While Arkansas led the SEC in rushing, it was still one spot behind New Mexico State, which ranked seventh nationally in yards on the ground.

ARKANSAS 44, SMU 17

SEPTEMBER 19, 1998 *by Vic Harville*

Arkansas had lost to nonconference opponent SMU in the past three games in the series. This game marked the debut of Houston Nutt as head coach at Arkansas, a post he would hold for 10 years.

ARKANSAS 28, LOUISIANA-MONROE 27

SEPTEMBER 6, 2008 *by Dusty Higgins*

Having survived a scare in their previous game against nonconference opponent Western
Illinois, Arkansas hoped to establish their running game against Louisiana-Monroe.

ARKANSAS 14, SOUTHERN CALIFORNIA 50

SEPTEMBER 2, 2006 *by Dusty Higgins*

After suffering a humiliating 70-17 loss to Southern California the previous season, this game offered the Razorbacks a chance for redemption.

ARKANSAS 48, MISSOURI STATE 10

SEPTEMBER 5, 2009 *by Dusty Higgins*

The Missouri State game was the first to start quarterback Ryan Mallet, who had redshirted the previous year after transferring from Michigan.

ARKANSAS 58, MIDDLE TENNESSEE 6

OCTOBER 9, 1999 *by Vic Harville*

Having lost back-to-back SEC games, The Razorbacks couldn't have asked for a better nonconference game to regain their confidence. Middle Tennessee was ranked last nationally (114) in points allowed per game and 113 in total defense.

ARKANSAS 63, NEW MEXICO STATE 13

SEPTEMBER 4, 2004 *by Matt Haney*

In the first game of the 2004 season, Arkansas' depth chart had 16 players listed who had two or fewer career starts. For 11 players, it would be their first career start.

ARKANSAS 42, TEXAS A&M 38

OCTOBER 1, 2011 *by Dusty Higgins*

With both teams losing their previous week's games, each desperately needed a victory. Adding to that was former Southwest Conference foe Texas A&M's pending arrival to the Southeastern Conference next season, which made this game feel like it should mean a little more than the average nonconference game.

THE BATTLE
OF THE BOOT

The Battle of the Boot is considered one of the most dramatic games in college football, always held at the end of the regular season. You can almost smell the gumbo as you turn the pages in this chapter. Arkansas against LSU achieved classic rivalry status, and the artists approached the sense of urgency and importance with class and dignity.

—*Wally Hall, Assistant Managing Editor/Sports for the* Arkansas Democrat-Gazette

ARKANSAS 24, LSU 55

NOVEMBER 28, 2003 *by Matt Haney*

After three SEC losses earlier in the season and no hope for an SEC West title, Arkansas could still spoil LSU's chances at an SEC title game.

ARKANSAS 31, LSU 30

NOVEMBER 28, 2008 *by Dusty Higgins*

The Razorbacks, 4-7 after having lost to Mississippi State and saying goodbye to any chance at a bowl game the previous week, prepared to play an LSU team that was 7-4 and out of the national rankings for the first time since 2002.

ARKANSAS 31, LSU 23

NOVEMBER 27, 2010 *by Dusty Higgins*

A victory for LSU would have almost certainly guaranteed a Bowl Championship Series at-large berth, while a victory for Arkansas would provide the Hogs with the chance to claim the program's first BCS game.

ARKANSAS 41, LSU 14

NOVEMBER 27, 1998 *by Vic Harville*

Having gone 8-0, then losing its previous two games (including a loss to Mississippi State that would end its chances at going to the SEC Championship game), a win against 4-6 LSU would allow Arkansas to finish as co-champion of the SEC West.

ARKANSAS 17,
LSU 41

NOVEMBER 25, 2011 *by Dusty Higgins*

No. 3 Arkansas faced No. 1 LSU in a game that would not only have an impact on the SEC title game, but also the BCS national championship game. The recent and unexpected death of tight end Garrett Uekman (No. 88) the previous Sunday served as a rallying point for underdog Arkansas.

ARKANSAS 30,
LSU 33 (OT)

NOVEMBER 28, 2009 *by Dusty Higgins*

LSU had lost tight games to Florida and Alabama with an end-of-game meltdown 25-23 loss at Ole Miss that had put Les Miles under considerable heat for play-calling and clock management. After rising from a 3-4 start to take the SEC lead in total offense, passing and scoring, Arkansas was hoping Miles' misfortune continued.

ARKANSAS 50, LSU 48 (3 OT)

NOVEMBER 23, 2007 *by Dusty Higgins*

Rumors were that this could be the last game with their respective teams for Arkansas coach Houston Nutt and LSU coach Les Miles. Miles was also getting some grief for his pronunciation of Arkansas at a recent press conference, in which he called it "Ar-Kansas."

ARKANSAS 14, LSU 3

NOVEMBER 24, 2000 *by Matt Haney*

For the second time since Arkansas joined the SEC, both Arkansas (5-5) and LSU (7-3) entered their final season game with postseason and championship implications.

ARKANSAS 14, LSU 43

NOVEMBER 26, 2004 *by Matt Haney*

Under coach Houston Nutt, the Razorbacks were 17-0 and undefeated in Little Rock at War Memorial Stadium going into the game against No. 14 LSU.

ARKANSAS 26, LSU 31

NOVEMBER 24, 2006 *by Dusty Higgins*

With a 10-game winning streak and a No. 6 BCS ranking, the Razorbacks were confident heading into the game against No. 10 LSU.

CALLING OUT THE COACHES

When a game called for the coaches to be the center of attention, there has always been a creative flair because the tone of the game was going to be set by the coaches' personalities as much as the action. Always clever and always creative, this chapter will leave a feeling of nostalgia and anticipation for the next game.

—Wally Hall, Assistant Managing Editor/Sports for the Arkansas Democrat-Gazette

ARKANSAS 38, ALABAMA 41

SEPTEMBER 15, 2007 *by Dusty Higgins*

Despite 16th ranked Arkansas' stout rushing duo, Darren McFadden and Felix Jones, Alabama was considered a three-point favorite over Arkansas in this early season matchup.

ARKANSAS 20, KENTUCKY 21

OCTOBER 18, 2008 *by Dusty Higgins*

Bobby Petrino's 4-0 record at Louisville against Kentucky along with the team's first SEC victory the previous week helped bolster confidence going into the game against the Wildcats.

ARKANSAS 21, OLE MISS 23

OCTOBER 25, 2008 *by Dusty Higgins*

Former head coach Houston Nutt's return to Razorback Stadium as the Ole Miss head coach was much anticipated by fans who were eager to show Nutt that they were better off without him.

ARKANSAS 28, OLE MISS 17

NOVEMBER 12, 2005 *by Dusty Higgins*

For the first time in eight seasons under coach Houston Nutt, the Razorbacks went into a game knowing they had no chance for a winning record or a bowl game.

ARKANSAS 58, UTEP 21

NOVEMBER 13, 2010 *by Dusty Higgins*

The Razorbacks were a four-touchdown favorite for their final nonconference game against the Miners, coached by Mike Price, former mentor of Arkansas coach Bobby Petrino.

ARKANSAS 14, ALABAMA 49

SEPTEMBER 20, 2008 *by Dusty Higgins*

This game marked the first meeting between NFL refugee coaches, Arkansas' Bobby Petrino and Alabama's Nick Saban, billed as resident offensive and defensive geniuses, respectively.

ARKANSAS 20, UTAH STATE 0

SEPTEMBER 9, 2006 *by Dusty Higgins*

After living through a second humiliating defeat by Southern California, the Razorbacks were able to take a break with an easy win against Utah State. This game marked Mitch Mustain's debut at quarterback and was Gus Malzahn's second game (the first, a 50-14 loss to Southern California) as the Razorbacks' new offensive coordinator.

ARKANSAS 44, MISSISSIPPI STATE 10

NOVEMBER 19, 2005 *by Dusty Higgins*

With just one SEC win that season, the Razorbacks faced a Mississippi State team that was winless in the SEC. In the previous game against Ole Miss, Houston famously cackled, "...I called it, Chuck!" during a post-game question from Chuck Barrett about whether a fourth-quarter touchdown play was called from the sideline or was an audible by quarterback Casey Dick.

ARKANSAS 46, TROY 26

SEPTEMBER 1, 2007 *by Dusty Higgins*

After an off-season filled with controversy, which ended with offensive coordinator Gus Malzahn leaving for Tulsa and heralded freshman quarterback Mitch Mustain transferring to Southern California after a disparaging e-mail from a booster with ties to the Houston Nutt family, the Razorbacks were more than ready to get back to playing football.

ARKANSAS 30, TULSA 23

NOVEMBER 1, 2008 *by Dusty Higgins*

After losing their previous game to former head coach Houston Nutt at Ole Miss, the Razorbacks now faced former offensive coach Gus Malzahn and an 8-0 Tulsa team.

ARKANSAS 28, NORTHEAST LOUISIANA* 16

*Northeast Louisiana changed their name to Louisiana-Monroe in 1999.

SEPTEMBER 6, 1997 by Vic Harville

After a dismal previous season, the Razorbacks, with coach Danny Ford's best recruiting class, were hopeful that this game would mark the start of a new winning era for the team.

ARKANSAS 66, NORTH TEXAS 7

SEPTEMBER 29, 2007 *by Dusty Higgins*

With a winless team and his back against the wall, Houston Nutt needed a win to keep fans satisfied with the his job performance. A Sunbelt team like North Texas was just what the doctor ordered.

ARKANSAS 17, OLE MISS 30

OCTOBER 24, 2009 *by Dusty Higgins*

Arkansas was still reeling from nearly pulled off an upset in their previous week's game against No. 1 Florida, during which they endured a disproportionate number of penalties that led to the suspension of the officiating crew. Meanwhile Ole Miss, headed by former coach Houston Nutt, was having its best start in six seasons.

ARKANSAS 29, OLE MISS 24

OCTOBER 22, 2011 *by Dusty Higgins*

The No. 9 Razorbacks resumed their push for an upper-tier bowl as they faced a Rebel team that had lost nine consecutive SEC games under coach Houston Nutt.

ARKANSAS 34, AUBURN 10

OCTOBER 30, 1999 *by Vic Harville*

Arkansas had played two relatively weak teams in its previous two games coupled with a bye week, and Auburn, coached by Tommy Tuberville, promised to be the first real challenge to the Razorbacks since their Oct. 3 loss to Kentucky.

ARKANSAS 28, WESTERN ILLINOIS 24

AUGUST 30, 2008 *by Dusty Higgins*

The opening game of the 2008 season brought forth a much anticipated
Razorback team with a retooled offense spearheaded by coach Bobby Petrino.

ARKANSAS 20, GEORGIA 23

OCTOBER 22, 2005 *by Dusty Higgins*

At 2-4 with a 0-3 SEC record, the Razorbacks needed a break. Instead they were playing through the second-toughest schedule in the nation, and had to face a No. 4 Georgia team (6-0) competing for the national championship.

POSITIONING THE PLAYERS

Games always come down to the players and how they execute, but getting to know their personalities was just as important as awareness of their playing ability. More times than not, and that's true with every chapter of this great book, a background was set that gave appropriate measure of what the teams faced that day. These sports/editorial cartoons have become a legacy of the *Arkansas Democrat-Gazette*.

—*Wally Hall, Assistant Managing Editor/Sports for the* Arkansas Democrat-Gazette

ARKANSAS 34, TENNESSEE-CHATTANOOGA 15

OCTOBER 6, 2007 *by Dusty Higgins*

Excitement was building with Darren McFadden 154 rushing yards away from breaking the record of 3,570 career rushing yards set by Ben Cowins 29 years earlier. McFadden would end the game 32 yards shy of the record.

ARKANSAS 20, FLORIDA 23

OCTOBER 17, 2009 *by Dusty Higgins*

Injury-plagued Arkansas headed to the Swamp to face No. 1 Florida, where there was very little expectation that Arkansas would come out on top.

ARKANSAS 13, TENNESSEE 34

NOVEMBER 10, 2007 *by Dusty Higgins*

Arkansas had been using the WildHog formation to great success, thanks in large part to players Darren "D-Mac" McFadden and Felix "The Cat" Jones.

ARKANSAS 52, NEW MEXICO 3

SEPTEMBER 10, 2011 *by Dusty Higgins*

The Warren Trio, consisting of wide receivers Greg Childs and Jarius Wright, and tight end Chris Gragg, all grew up in Warren, Ark., and led the No. 14 Razorbacks' fast-break offense as the team faced New Mexico at War Memorial Stadium in Little Rock.

ARKANSAS 45, MISSISSIPPI STATE 31

NOVEMBER 17, 2007 *by Dusty Higgins*

After rushing for 4,191 yards in 35 games, more than any runner in Razorback history, the buzz was on about Darren McFadden's Heisman chances. That the Mississippi State game was being played in War Memorial Stadium, where McFadden had so many signature performances, was icing on the cake.

CONFERENCE RIVAL RAMPAGE

When the Razorbacks and South Carolina joined the Southeastern Conference in 1992 they were made permanent opponents, so the Hogs have played the Gamecocks more than any other Eastern Division team. It is a series that grew even more interesting the few years Lou Holtz, who coached at Arkansas for seven seasons, was the head coach at South Carolina. Missouri will replace South Carolina as the Hogs' permanent opponent in 2014, but the impact of those games will not be forgotten.

—*Wally Hall, Assistant Managing Editor/Sports for the* Arkansas Democrat-Gazette

ARKANSAS 41, SOUTH CAROLINA 20

NOVEMBER 6, 2010 *by Dusty Higgins*

A win over Arkansas would have given South Carolina a lead in the SEC East Division, while Arkansas — with Auburn, Alabama, and LSU ahead of it in the West — was looking at increasing its bowl standing with a victory.

ARKANSAS 44, SOUTH CAROLINA 28

NOVEMBER 5, 2011 *by Dusty Higgins*

On any other day, No. 7 Arkansas versus No. 9 South Carolina would have attracted the ESPN GameDay crew and received coast-to-coast coverage. Unfortunately, No. 1 LSU was visiting No. 2 Alabama in the first 1 vs. 2 regular-season matchup of SEC teams.

ARKANSAS 48, SOUTH CAROLINA 36

NOVEMBER 3, 2007 *by Dusty Higgins*

Arkansas' (5-3) games had fallen into two categories by the time they played South Carolina (6-3). The Razorbacks either had blowout games or close games, and they were 0-3 with fourth-quarter leads in each of those late losses.

ARKANSAS 33, SOUTH CAROLINA 16

NOVEMBER 7, 2009 *by Dusty Higgins*

The game against South Carolina was a "must-win" for a 4-4 Arkansas team if they wanted to be bowl-eligible in their second year under coach Bobby Petrino.

ARKANSAS 48, SOUTH CAROLINA 14

OCTOBER 16, 1999 *by Vic Harville*

South Carolina was on a 16-game losing streak, six under coach Lou Holtz, who coached the Razorbacks from 1977-83 before being forced out.

ARKANSAS 28, SOUTH CAROLINA 6

NOVEMBER 6, 2003 *by Matt Haney*

Less than a week after getting a seven-overtime victory against Kentucky and breaking a three-game losing streak in the SEC, Arkansas was playing conference rival South Carolina.

ARKANSAS 32, SOUTH CAROLINA 35

NOVEMBER 6, 2004 *by Matt Haney*

After a three-game losing streak, Arkansas was desperate for a win with bowl hopes contingent on the Razorbacks winning three out of their final four games against conference opponents South Carolina, Ole Miss, Mississippi State and LSU.

ARKANSAS 26, SOUTH CAROLINA 20

NOVEMBER 4, 2006 *by Dusty Higgins*

In its first primetime ESPN game since suffering a 50-14 loss to Southern California (USC), after coming off
a 70-17 loss to Southern California a year earlier, Arkansas played a much tamer USC in South Carolina.

ARKANSAS 41, SOUTH CAROLINA 28

OCTOBER 17, 1998 *by Vic Harville*

At 5-0 and one of just 12 undefeated teams in major college football, the Razorbacks were sitting pretty. A win over South Carolina would tie Arkansas with Mississippi State atop the SEC West.

STUCK ON THE DRAWING BOARD

For every cartoon that makes it into the pages of the *Arkansas Democrat-Gazette*, there are a handful of cartoons that are not chosen by the editors. I typically draw two or three ideas for each game-day cartoon and let the editor decide what best fits the theme of the game-day story. Some of the cartoons included here were never really serious contenders for a game-day cartoon. At the beginning of a season, I'll often draw cartoons just to help put me in the zone and, having no limits or boundaries, they are often filled with levels of my own overconfidence (when they're playing bad) or depression (when they're playing really bad). These rarely make it to the newspaper page.

—*Dusty Higgins, Graphic Artist for the* Arkansas Democrat-Gazette